Mighty Mighty **MONSTERS**

The KING of HALLOWEEN CASTLE

created by Sean O'Reilly
illustrated by Arcana Studio

www.raintreepublishers.co.uk
Visit our website to find out
more information about
Raintree books.

To order:
☎ Phone 0845 6044371
🖷 Fax +44 (0) 1865 312263
🖳 Email myorders@raintreepublishers.co.uk

Customers from outside the UK please telephone +44 1865 312262

Raintree is an imprint of Capstone Global Library Limited,
a company incorporated in England and Wales having its registered
office at 7 Pilgrim Street, London, EC4V 6LB
– Registered company number: 6695582

First published by Stone Arch Books in 2010
First published in the United Kingdom in paperback in 2012
The moral rights of the proprietor have been asserted.

Edited by Laura Knowles
Originated by Capstone Global Library Ltd
Printed and bound in China

ISBN 978 1 406 23719 1 (paperback)
16 15 14 13
10 9 8 7 6 5 4 3

British Library Cataloguing in Publication Data
A full catalogue record for this book is available
from the British Library.

In a strange corner of the world known as Transylmania . . .

Legendary monsters were born.

WELCOME TO TRANSYLMANIA

But long before their frightful fame, these classic creatures faced fears of their own.

To take on terrifying teachers and homework horrors, they formed the most fearsome friendship on Earth . . .

Mighty Mighty MONSTERS

Vlad

Talbot

Witchita

Milton

Poto

Frankie

Igor

Mary

Why would anyone need all these weapons?
Maybe he's a collector?
Then I'd hate to know his other hobbies.
Come on, guys. We have to find Samhain.
And I know we're on the right track.

The Flame of Halloween has burnt out!
Without the flame, Halloween will no longer be spooky.
Right. So can you help us?
Sure, we just have to relight the flame before trick-or-treating begins.

Uh, I believe it's already started.
Yeah, most kids head out right after dinner.

Then there is no time to waste! Follow me!

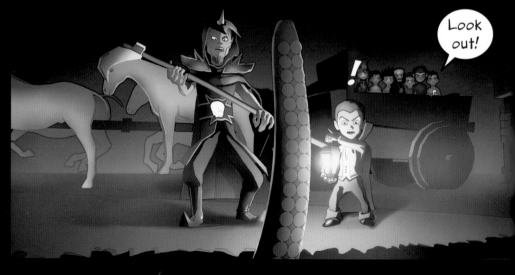

36

The world is a better place when it's scary, don't you think?
I couldn't have said it better myself.

SPOOKY
FOREST

MONSTER
SCHOOL

FLAME OF
HALLOWEEN

CASTLE OF
DOOM

Mighty Mighty MONSTERS

...BEFORE THEY WERE STARS!

FRANKIE AND MARY

Nicknames: Frank and M.

Hometown: Transylmania

Favourite colours: red and yellow

Mighty mighty powers: superhuman strength; ability to smash through concrete with a single blow; able to lift ten times their body weight; together, their powers are doubled.

BIOGRAPHIES

Growing up as neighbours in Transylmania, Frankie and Mary quickly discovered that they had more in common than green skin. Both of their parents were scientists, who "developed" their children into powerful monsters. Soon, Frankie and Mary looked for a way to channel their superhuman strengths — and the Mighty Mighty Monsters were the perfect fit. Later in life, the two friends married and became Hollywood's first superpowered creature couple.

In 1818, author Mary Shelley published *Frankenstein*, the first book about the famous green monster. Shelley said the idea came to her in a dream.

In 1931, actor Boris Karloff played Frankenstein in the film of Shelley's novel. Although the monster's looks have changed many times, this became the most popular version of the creepy creature.

A few years later, in 1935, a sequel to the *Frankenstein* film was released, titled *The Bride of Frankenstein*. In this film, the green beast is finally married.

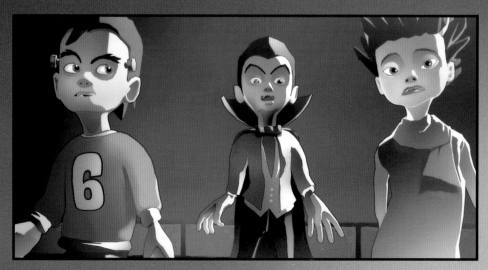

ABOUT SEAN O'REILLY
AND ARCANA STUDIO

As a lifelong comics fan, Sean O'Reilly dreamed of becoming a comic book creator. In 2004, he realized that dream by creating Arcana Studio. In one short year, O'Reilly took his studio from a one-person operation in his house to an award-winning comic book publisher with more than 150 graphic novels produced for Harper Collins, Simon & Schuster, Random House, Scholastic, and others.

Within a year, the company won many awards including the Shuster Award for Outstanding Publisher and the Moonbeam Award for top children's graphic novel. O'Reilly also won the Top 40 Under 40 award from the city of Vancouver and authored The Clockwork Girl for Top Graphic Novel at Book Expo America in 2009.

Currently, O'Reilly is one of the most prolific independent comic book writers in Canada. While showing no signs of slowing down in comics, he now also writes screenplays and adapts his creations for the big screen.

GLOSSARY

amuse make someone laugh or smile

collector person who collects something as a hobby

electrifying act of shocking something with electricity or making someone excited

hobby something that you enjoy doing in your spare time

introduce tell the name of one person to another person

moat deep, wide ditch dug around a fort, castle, or town and filled with water to prevent attacks

nickname descriptive, friendly, or jokey name used with, or instead of, a person's real name

passage hall or corridor

solution answer to a problem

terror very great fear

torture extreme pain or mental suffering

DISCUSSION QUESTIONS

1. Before they met Samhain, the Mighty Mighty Monsters were afraid of him. Have you ever judged someone without actually meeting them? Explain.

2. The Mighty Mighty Monsters are a team. Who do you think is the leader? Do you think every team needs a leader? Explain.

3. All of the Mighty Mighty Monsters are different. Which character do you like the best? Why?

WRITING PROMPTS

1. Imagine a brand new member of the Mighty Mighty Monsters. What superpowers would your monster have? What would it look like? Write about your Mighty Mighty Monster, and then draw a picture of it.

2. Write a story about your favourite Halloween. Where did you go? What costume did you wear? Did you eat any special food?

3. Write your own Mighty Mighty Monsters adventure. What will the ghoulish gang do next? What villains will they face? You decide.

INFORMATION BOOKS

Ghosts and Other Spectres (Dark Side), Anita
Ganeri (Wayland, 2010)

The Mystery of Vampires and Werewolves
(Can Science Solve?), Chris Oxlade (Heinemann
Library, 2008)

GRAPHIC NOVELS

Dracula (Graphic Revolve), Bram Stoker, retold by
Michael Burgan (Raintree, 2009)

Frankenstein (Graphic Revolve), Mary Shelley, retold
by Michael Burgan (Raintree, 2009)

The Phantom of the Opera (Graphic Chillers), Gaston
Leroux, retold by Joeming Dunn (Franklin Watts, 2010)

WEBSITE

learnenglishkids.britishcouncil.org/en/make-
your-own/make-your-monster
Visit this website to create your own monster. You can
also invent your own scary story, dangerous animal,
or superhero.

Mighty Mighty MONSTERS

ADVENTURES

Monster Mansion
ISBN: 978 1 406 23721 4

New Monster in School
ISBN: 978 1 406 23723 8

Hide and Shriek
ISBN: 978 1 406 23718 4

My Missing Monster
ISBN: 978 1 406 23722 1

Lost in Spooky Forest
ISBN: 978 1 406 23720 7